My Special Mascot Friend is

Damon and mom

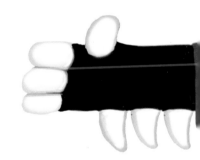

Al the Octopus
is amazing.

How *does* he keep his
tentacles untangled?

NHL MASCOTS & Friends

WRITTEN BY
Holly Preston

ILLUSTRATED BY
James Hearne

Always Books Ltd.

NHL Mascots & Friends

Text and illustrations © 2019 NHL
All Rights Reserved.

Manufactured by Friesens Corporation in Altona, MB, Canada
January 2019
Job #247054

ISBN: 978-0-9951990-8-8

Layout by James Hearne

Editing by Visible Ink Incorporated

AFANFORLIFE.COM™

Bailey boldly announces he is "King of the rink."

Spartacat roars, "No, that's me!"

Bernie is so brave, his team won't get snowed under.

Harvey is the most hilarious hound...

... his tongue just gets twisted around and around!

Blades and Louie know the "bear" facts of hockey...

... they never hibernate when there's a game to be played.

Carlton gives bear hugs
when it's time for bed.

Fin has a whale of a time. The Canucks are his team.

Come cheer them on (but don't lose your head!)

Gnash is a prankster—
(I hope you like pie).

The Moose takes control—
he likes to fly high!

N.J. Devil is a devilish guy,
but he's friendly to fans
who want to high five!

Nordy is unique.

His style is so wild!

S.J. Sharkie is the hardest working fish in the NHL. That makes him so hungry!

Oh, what is there to eat?

Spectacular Slapshot soars
above all the rest.

A hockey Gila monster named Chance has one foot in the desert and one on the ice. That's nice.

Sparky loves to play hockey. Just look and see why!

Stanley C. Panther is on the prowl for the Cup.

Then you see Stinger and wonder what's up?

Stormy seems calm
but watch out for
what's brewing!

Lightning strikes when
ThunderBug steps on the ice.

Iceburgh is the coolest dancing penguin on Earth.

Sabretooth sees the game like nobody else.

Would upside-down hockey be so hard to play?

Tommy Hawk is so proud
of his team.

It looks like
you are, too!

Wild Wing makes an
entrance.
You'll know he's arrived.

Quack!
Quack!

Gritty's a mystery and
quite a clumsy guy.
He stands up for his team
with his googly eyes.

Hunter's a lynx.
He just loves hockey hijinks.

Victor E. Green has come to play from an alien place far away.

Youppi! has a party for all his friends.
You're invited to attend!

Yippee and
hooray!
You won't want
it to end.

AUTOGRAPHS

AUTOGRAPHS

ABOUT THE AUTHOR
Holly Preston

Holly Preston is a journalist who worked for CTV and CBC. She grew up watching NHL hockey with her brother and father. Now she creates children's picture books for professional sports teams. She hopes young NHL fans will enjoy having a book that celebrates the mascot of their home team.

ABOUT THE ILLUSTRATOR
James Hearne

Born in London England, James began his art career at the tender age of eight, selling drawings to guests at his grandparents' hotel. He continues to sell his whimsical illustrations around the globe as a full-time illustrator and full-time hockey fan.